Fun Fact File

Contents

There are 10 pairs of glasses like these hidden in this book. Can you find them? Most of the Biff, Chip and Kipper Stories have a pair of glasses in an odd place. Find out why on page 31.

OXFORD
UNIVERSITY PRESS

Meet the Robinson family

Biff

Biff likes playing football and going swimming. She is always ready to join in with any game and she likes making things, but don't give her anything to hold as she might drop it!

Chip

Chip likes cycling and sports. He is very good at drawing and if you want anything painting, ask Chip, as he is very careful.

Biff and Chip

Biff and Chip are twins. Biff's real name is Elizabeth. Chip's real name is David. So why are they called Biff and Chip? Because when Kipper was little he couldn't say Elizabeth or Beth. He said Biff. And he couldn't say David. He said Chip. Chip doesn't sound like David, but that is what Kipper said and everyone laughed so the nicknames stuck!

Kipper

Kipper likes to play with Biff, Chip and Floppy. Sometimes he gets into trouble. His real name is Christopher, but when he was learning to talk he couldn't say Christopher and it sounded like Kipper. Dad decided that the name Kipper suited him so now everyone calls him Kipper.

Mum

Mum likes playing sports and taking Floppy for long walks. She is very good at DIY and can fix almost anything!

Dad

Dad likes playing games and trying to trick Biff, Chip and Kipper. He always tries to help, but things don't always turn out as he intends!

Turn to page 22 to find out how Floppy got his name.

Floppy

Floppy is a big soppy dog. He loves playing with a stick or a ball and running all over the place. He loves to dig holes or to go for a swim in the pond. He often ends up covered in mud!

Gran

Gran is Mum's mother. She loves coming to visit and spending time with the children, but she is always getting into trouble!

Funny fish

Mum, Dad, Biff, Chip, Kipper and Floppy go fishing.

They get a crab...

...an octopus...

...a bucket...

...and a boot!

Floppy gets a fish!

5

Help Floppy!

Which path will take Floppy to his bone?

1

2

3

4

The answer can be found on page 32.

Meet the friends

Wilf

Wilf is the same age as Biff and Chip and he is in their class at school. Wilf likes to play football and he loves riding his bike.

Wilma

Wilma is Wilf's sister. She is a year older than Biff and Chip and is in the class above them at school. Wilma is good at thinking up new games and she always knows what to do. She wants to be a musician when she grows up.

Wilf and Wilma

Wilf and Wilma live two doors away from Biff and Chip so it is easy for them to play together after school and at weekends.

Anneena

Anneena is in the same class as Biff, Chip, Wilf and Nadim at school. Anneena is very good at making things and is always full of good ideas.
It is hard to beat Anneena at any sport.

Nadim

Nadim is in the same class as Biff, Chip, Wilf and Anneena at school. He loves telling jokes and making everyone laugh. Nadim likes reading and numbers, but most of all he loves his computer.
He is very good at computer games.

The neighbourhood

Can you see?

- Floppy
- A motorbike
- Four green cars
- A slide
- A tree house
- A person cycling
- People playing golf
- The wooden bridge over the stream

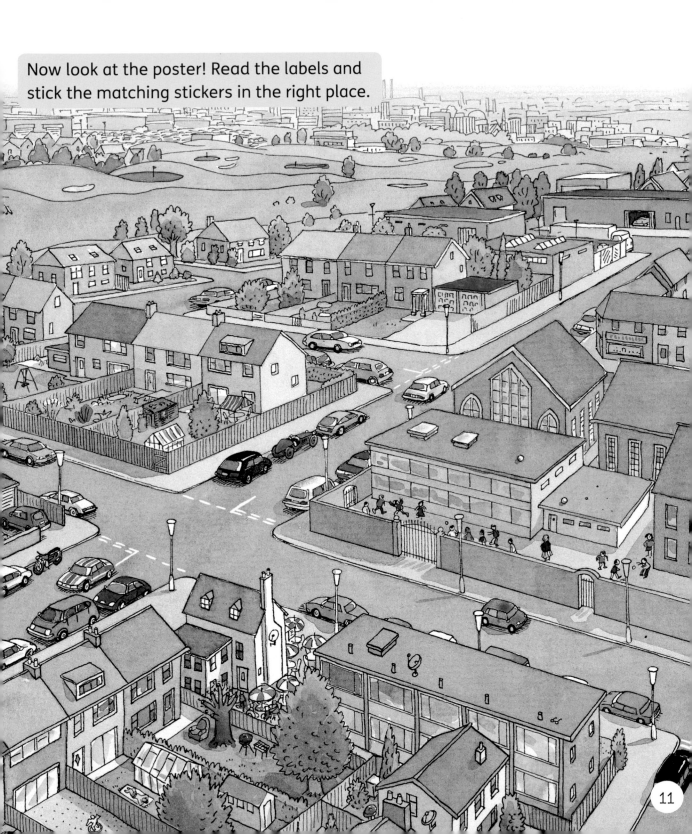

Now look at the poster! Read the labels and stick the matching stickers in the right place.

11

Fun facts

Biff

Age: 7

School: Ortree Primary School

Likes: making things, swimming

Dislikes: wearing dresses

Favourite colour: red

I am good at: football and skateboarding

I want to be: a geologist (an expert in rocks)

Chip

Age: 7

School: Ortree Primary School

Likes: art, cycling

Dislikes: quarrelling

Favourite colour: blue

I am good at: painting and finding things

I want to be: an artist

Kipper

Age: 4

School: Ortree Primary School

Likes: playing with Floppy

Dislikes: tidying up

Favourite colour: orange

I am good at: making friends

I want to be: an astronaut

Floppy

Age: 9 (or 63 in dog years)

School: obedience training

Likes: sleeping, playing fetch

Dislikes: baths

Favourite place: the park

Favourite meal: a bone

I am good at: barking and getting muddy

Kipper's scrapbook

Kipper made a scrapbook of his first day at school.

I look smart.

This is my peg.

We did hand prints.

We had fun dressing up.

I had fun with sand.

Make a scrapbook of your day.

Make your own characters

Trace, colour and cut out the characters.

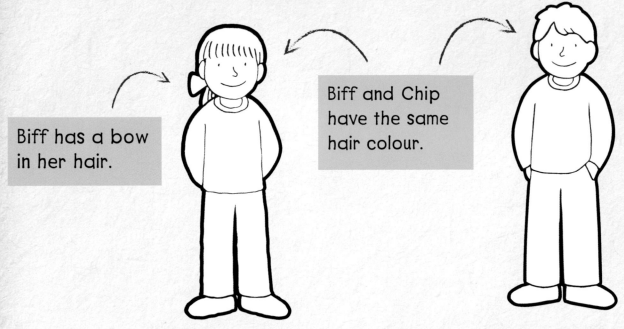

Biff has a bow in her hair.

Biff and Chip have the same hair colour.

Add stripes to Kipper's top when you colour him in.

What colour is Floppy?

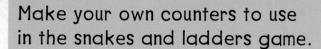
Make your own counters to use in the snakes and ladders game.

You will need:
A4 paper
A pencil
Felt-tip pens, crayons or colouring pencils. Scissors

1. Ask an adult to help you.
2. Put a piece of paper on top of a character and trace the outline of the character on to your paper.
3. Add the details of the character's face and clothes.
4. Colour in your character.
5. Cut out your character.

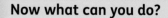

Now what can you do?

Make pencil puppets – stick a pencil or lolly stick to the back of the character with sticky tape. Use the characters to retell a Biff, Chip and Kipper story you have read or to make up your own story.

Make a shoebox theatre – stick your character on to card and add a tab at the bottom. Fold the ends of the tab back to make the character stand up. Tell your own stories using the characters. You could make scenery too.

Make a collage – create a collage all about Biff, Chip and Kipper.

Snakes and ladders

You will need:
- A counter for each player
- A dice

How to play:
- Take it in turns. Pick a player to start.
- Roll the dice. Move the counter the number of squares shown on the dice. If you land on a ladder, go up to the top of it. If you land on a snake, go down to the end of it.
- The first player to get to the finish is the winner.

Spot the difference

Can you see 4 differences each time?

Summer

Autumn

Winter

The answers can be found on page 32.

Kipper's cake recipe

Don't make this at home!

Ingredients

Cornflakes
Tomato sauce
Milk
Jam
Sugar
Baked beans

Equipment

A big bowl
A spoon

What to do

1. Put the cornflakes into the bowl. Add a big squirt of tomato sauce.

2. Add some milk and a big dollop of jam.

3. Add sugar and a bowl of baked beans.

4. Mix it all up.

5. Give it to your friends.

Kipper made a cake for his toys. Even Floppy would not eat it.
Try making the cakes on the next page instead!

Make your own cornflake cakes

Ingredients

- 50g butter
- 150g chocolate (you can use milk or dark chocolate)
- 100g cornflakes
- 3 tablespoons of golden syrup

Equipment

- An adult to help you
- Measuring scales
- Tablespoon
- Saucepan
- Mixing bowl
- Wooden spoon
- 12 cupcake cases

What to do:

1. Weigh out the ingredients using the measuring scales.
2. Break the chocolate into chunks.
3. Put the butter, chocolate and golden syrup into a saucepan.
4. Ask an adult to melt the butter, chocolate and golden syrup over a low heat.
5. Put the cornflakes into the mixing bowl.
6. Pour the chocolate mixture onto the cornflakes.
7. Stir it all together with a wooden spoon.
8. Spoon the mixture into the 12 cupcake cases. Try to get the same amount of mixture in each one!
9. Put them in the fridge for 1 hour.
10. Eat them!

You could use other cereal instead of cornflakes and add more yummy ingredients such as chopped-up marshmallows, raisins or other dried fruit.

How Floppy got his name

They got the dog home.

He ran in and out of the house.

He ran up and down the stairs.

He ran into the kitchen.

What shall we call him? I like Marmalade Mackintosh.

Prince?

Hector?

Where is he?

Everyone liked that name.
They called him Floppy.

Help Kipper to find Floppy

Can you help Kipper to find his way to Floppy?

Start

The snowman

The children are building a snowman. Can you find these things in the picture?

Things to look for: robin red nose

Now count the blackbirds you can see.

twig

scarf

spade

bike

Biff's hat hunt

Mum has lost her hat again. She has given Biff a list of places it could be. Can you follow the instructions, collect the letters and help Biff to find mum's hat?

Find the hat!

1. Go into the house. Turn left into the living room. Look on the chair.

2. Go to the kitchen. Go round the table and look next to it.

3. Go out of the back door and into the garden. Go across to the shed. Look behind it.

4. Go past the paddling pool and round the tree. Go straight down to the swing. Look next to it.

5. Go to the bins. Look behind them.

Use the letters to spell out where the hat is.

The answer can be found on page 32.

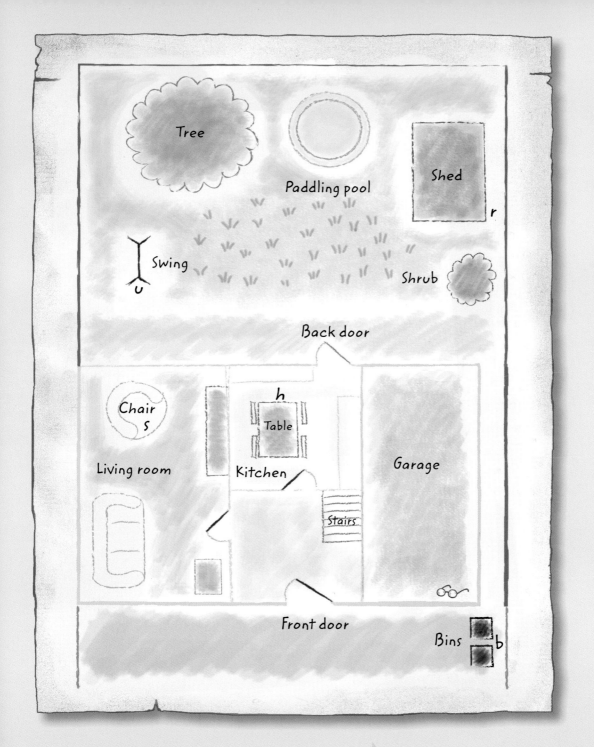

Tree

Paddling pool

Shed

r

Swing

u

Shrub

Back door

h

Table

Chair

s

Living room

Kitchen

Garage

Stairs

Front door

Bins

b

29

Kipper's best friend

When I feel lonely,
When I feel sad.
When I've been naughty,
Or when things look bad ...

When I am happy,
When things are fun.
When I've been good,
And Mum whispers "Well done!"

When I feel scared,
Or I'm not very well,
Then I've got a friend,
And it's *him* I can tell.

And who do I tell,
When I snuggle in bed?
I bet you can guess who!
Of course! It's my Ted.

Write a poem about your best friend.

Quiz

1. What is Chip's real name?
2. Who likes trying to play tricks on Biff, Chip and Kipper?
3. Who is in the same class as Biff and Chip at school?
4. How old is Floppy? (In human and dog years!)
5. What is Kipper's favourite colour?
6. Who likes swimming?
7. Which character is good at DIY?
8. What name did Kipper think of for the new dog?
9. Why do Biff and Chip have the same birthday?
10. What is Wilf's sister called?

The answers can be found on page 32.

The glasses

Why is there a pair of glasses hidden in most of the books?

I often go to a park where there is a notice saying 'Dogs must be kept on the lead'. I nearly always meet a dog off the lead, so clearly the dog is too short-sighted to read the notice.

So I buy old pairs of glasses from junk shops and when I meet a dog in the park I put a pair of glasses on him.

Of course, he shakes his head and they drop off sooner or later, so that is why there are pairs of glasses in odd places in my pictures.

Alex Brychta, illustrator

Answers

Page 6 *Help Floppy!* Path 3 takes Floppy to his bone.

Page 18 *Spot the difference*

Page 28 *Biff's hat hunt* - Mum's hat is in the shrub.

Page 31 *Quiz*

1. David **2.** Dad **3.** Wilf, Nadim and Anneena **4.** 9 or 63 **5.** Orange **6.** Biff
7. Mum **8.** Marmalade Mackintosh **9.** Because they are twins **10.** Wilma

---

Inspire a love of reading
with this companion to Biff, Chip
and Kipper Stories.

Introduce children to the much-loved
Robinson family and their friends. Have fun
whilst finding out more about Biff, Chip and
Kipper with abridged versions of popular
stories, games and things to make and do.

Packed with opportunities for talk and
discussion and lots of activities to develop
observation skills. Includes engaging activities
with hidden items to find, fun facts to read
and discuss, a board game to compete in,
mazes to puzzle over and creative activities to
inspire children.

Ideal for adults to share with children or for
children to explore independently. Perfect for
immersing children in the world of Biff, Chip
and Kipper!

The series creators

Author
Roderick Hunt MBE

Illustrator
Alex Brychta MBE

Rod and Alex are the award-winning author and
illustrator team responsible for creating one of the
most popular character series of all time.